CHRISTMAS CRAFTS FOR KIDS

CONTENTS

What You Will Need

In this book you'll find all sorts of imaginative ideas for Christmas. But before you begin any of the projects make sure you get together a few useful tools first. You'll need scissors or pinking shears for cutting (ask a grown up to cut thick card for you with a craft knife); a pair of compasses for making circles; a bradawl and a hole punch to make holes; glue, tape and staples to fix things together; and a needle and thread ready for sewing. Paint, felt-tip pens and fabric crayons will all come in useful for decorating.

needle and thread

clear glue

pliers

PVA glue and spreader

felt-tip pens

plastic tape

paint-brushes

clear tape

masking tape

double-sided tape

glitter glue

paint

Kitchen Equipment

To make the delicious Christmas biscuits and sweets on pages 10, 11 and 20-21 of this book, you will also need some standard kitchen tools including:

Pair of scales, measuring jug, measuring spoons, mixing bowls of various sizes, sieve, plastic spatula, cutlery, baking tray, greaseproof paper, chopping board, rolling pin, biscuit cutters, oven gloves.

Tubes of icing sugar, available in different colours from supermarkets and cake decorating shops, are a great way to decorate the biscuits.

safety pins

tracing paper

craft knife

thick card

pencil and eraser

metal ruler

pinking shears

scissors

bradawl

stapler and staples

hole punch

pair of compasses

fabric crayons

Remember

☆ Wear an apron and cover the work area.
☆ Collect together the items in the materials box at the beginning of each project.
☆ Always ask an adult for help when you see this sign [!]
☆ Clear up after yourself.

ruler

Christmas Tree

Begin the countdown to Christmas with this advent tree calendar.

Materials

24 wrapped sweets

24 15-cm lengths of ribbon

corrugated cardboard

sticky shapes

cocktail stick

tinsel

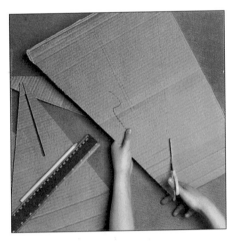

1 Mark 2 large triangles the same size on to corrugated cardboard. Mark a 5 mm slot from the centre to the top of one triangle and from the centre to the base of the other triangle. Cut out.

2 Paint the triangles green on both sides and leave to dry. Starting 5 cm from the base of one triangle, pierce 12 holes at regular intervals 1 cm from the edge along both sides.

3 Decorate both sides of both triangles with the sticky shapes. Slot the triangles together.

4 Securely tie a sweet to each piece of ribbon. Thread each ribbon through a hole and tie in a bow.

5 Glue tinsel to the other 2 edges of the tree.

Each day, from the first of December, take one sweet from the tree and eat it. When there are no more sweets left on the tree, it's Christmas Eve!

6 To make a star, trace off the template on page 38 on to card and paint yellow. When dry, paint all over with gold glitter paint. Attach to the tree with a cocktail stick.

7

Crackers for Christmas

To make your own Christmas crackers, all you need are a few readily-available materials and some good Christmas jokes. So get cracking!

Materials

wrapped sweets

2 gift rosettes

2 sparkly pipe cleaners

red and green crêpe paper

shiny tape

jokes

2 cardboard tubes

1 Use pinking shears to cut a piece of red crêpe paper twice as long as a cardboard tube. It should be wide enough to go around the tube with a 1 cm overlap. Cut a piece the same size from the green crêpe.

2 Fill the tubes with the wrapped sweets and add a joke.

Q. What is Father Christmas's cat called?

A. Santa Claws!

Did you hear about the Christmas robin for sale in the pet shop in January?

It was going cheap!

3 Cut out a piece of crêpe paper in each colour the same width as in step 1 but 2 cm shorter. Centre the smaller pieces of crêpe paper on top of the larger pieces.

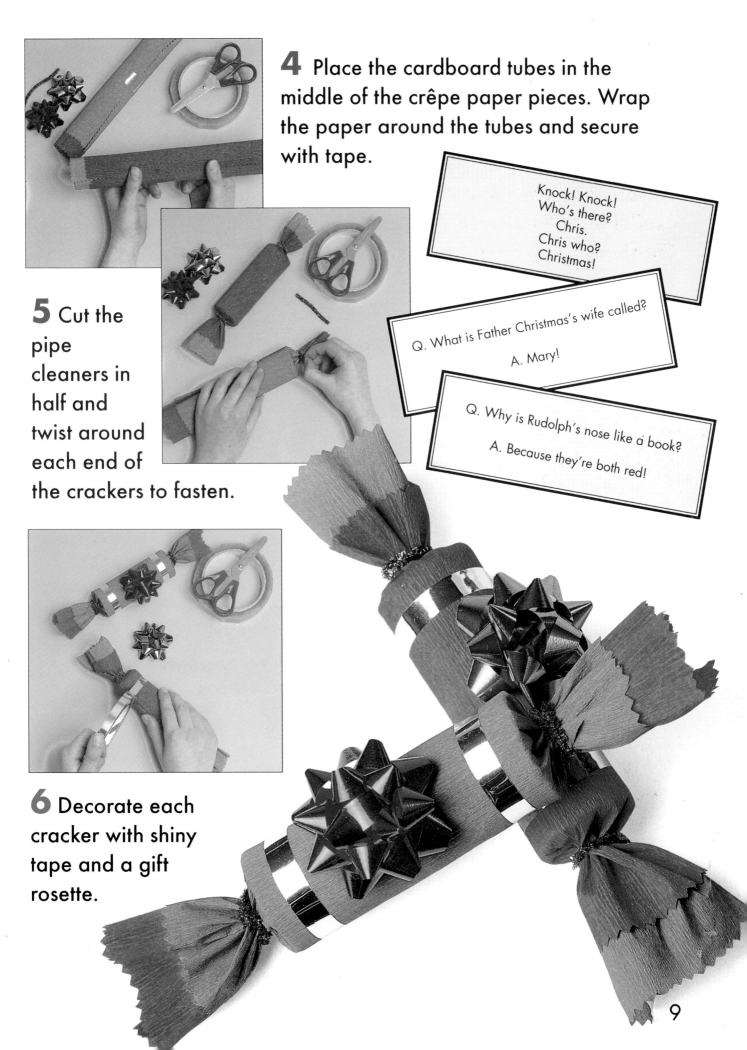

4 Place the cardboard tubes in the middle of the crêpe paper pieces. Wrap the paper around the tubes and secure with tape.

Knock! Knock!
Who's there?
Chris.
Chris who?
Christmas!

Q. What is Father Christmas's wife called?

A. Mary!

Q. Why is Rudolph's nose like a book?

A. Because they're both red!

5 Cut the pipe cleaners in half and twist around each end of the crackers to fasten.

6 Decorate each cracker with shiny tape and a gift rosette.

9

Truffle Puddings

Materials

sweet cases

25 g cocoa powder

50 g white chocolate

50 g cream cheese

25 g chopped glacé cherries

25 g currants

edible cake decorations

50 g icing sugar

Gift wrap each truffle pudding in a homemade box (see page 23) and give as a present. This mix makes 7.

1 Put the cream cheese, icing sugar, cocoa powder, currants and cherries into the mixing bowl and stir well to mix them all together.

2 Roll into small balls between your hands. Chill in the fridge for 30 minutes.

! 3 Melt the white chocolate in a heatproof bowl placed in a sauce-pan

of simmering water. Put a blob of melted chocolate on top of each sweet.

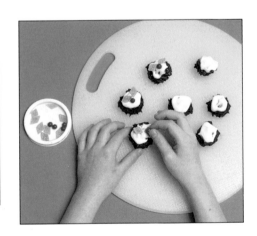

4 Decorate with the edible cake decorations.

Snowballs

To avoid a snowball fight, make lots of these sweets! This mix makes 7.

Materials

100 g white chocolate	50 g cream cheese	sweet cases
50 g ground almonds		
	50 g icing sugar	dessicated coconut

1 Stir the cream cheese, icing sugar and ground almonds together in a bowl until well mixed.

Keep in the fridge and eat within a week

2 Roll into small balls between your hands.

! **3** Melt the white chocolate in a heat-proof bowl in a saucepan of simmering water. First roll the balls in the chocolate and then in the dessicated coconut.

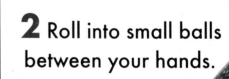

11

A Holly Wreath

No home is complete at Christmas without a holly wreath on the front door. This one can be used from year to year.

Materials

glitter

red salt dough (see page 40)

wide red ribbon

narrow red ribbon

2 baubles

tinsel

florists' fine gauge wire

2 sprigs holly

1 On a lightly-floured board, roll the salt dough into a thick sausage shape about 30 cm long. Make a hole with a pencil at one end of the sausage and model the other end into a point.

! 2 Place on to a greased baking tray and form into a circle. Moisten the pointed end and put into the hole. Smooth the join. Score the top of the ring with a plastic knife. Bake in the oven for 3-4 hours at 120°C/350°F/Gas mark ½ until firm, turning occasionally.

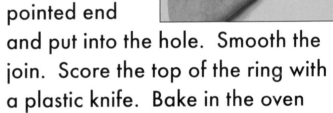

3 Lightly spread glue across the top of the ring and sprinkle on the glitter. Stick tinsel around the edge.

4 Thread the baubles on to the florists' wire. Twist the wire to keep them in place. Position the baubles on the bottom edge of the circle and secure by firmly winding the wire around the dough circle.

5 To hide the wire, wrap the wide ribbon between the baubles and tie into a bow. Glue the ends of the holly sprigs and tuck into the bow.

The finished wreath, ready to hang up on your door.

6 Thread the narrow ribbon through the top of the circle and knot to make a loop for hanging up the decoration. Tie the ribbon ends into a bow.

Musical Greetings

Ring out a seasonal message with this simple-to-make card.

Materials

coloured foil

corrugated cardboard

2 small bells

A4 sheet of thin card

50 cm ribbon

glitter glue

1 Punch 2 holes in the top of the corrugated cardboard. Trace off the bell template on page 38, centre over a hole and transfer the outline. Repeat. Cut out the 2 bells.

2 Cover the cardboard bells with foil, and stick down with glue. Sew a real bell to the bottom of each.

3 Cut the piece of A4 card in half lengthways. Take one piece and fold in half. Make 3 holes along the folded edge with a hole punch. (You can use the other half to make another card later.)

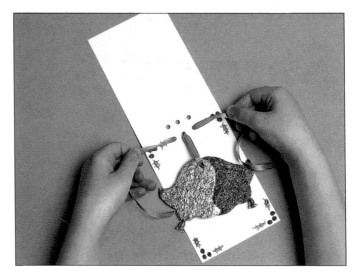

4 Decorate the front of the card with a border using first felt-tip pens, then glitter glue.

5 Thread the cardboard bells on to the ribbon. Open out the card and thread both ends of the ribbon through the centre hole. Thread each ribbon end back through the holes on either side and tie in a bow at the top.

The finished card will fit a standard-sized envelope. You can decorate the envelope with a pattern to match the card.

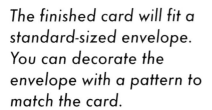

15

Surprise, Surprise!

It's no great surprise to receive a card at Christmas, unless it's one of these!

Materials

2 sheets A4 thin white card

small piece of sponge

glitter glue

sticky shapes

Pop-up snowman

1 Cut one sheet of card in half widthways. Fold the 2 pieces of card in half again.

2 Decorate the inside of one of the pieces of card by sponging with blue and white paint. Leave to dry.

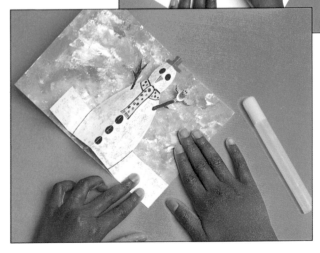

3 Trace off the snowman template on page 39 on to the outside of the other piece of card. Colour with felt-tip pens.

4 Fold back the tabs on the snowman and glue to the bottom corners of the sponged card.

Expanding tree

5 Cut a sheet of card in half lengthways. Fold one of the pieces in half. Now fold back one of the halves in half again. Open out.

6 Trace the tree template on page 39 on to the card taking care to position it correctly on the folds.

The finished cards. All that is left for you to do is to write on your own Christmas messages.

7 Paint and leave to dry. Decorate the tree with sticky shapes and glitter glue.

Mini Felt Stockings

The perfect present for the Christmas tree.

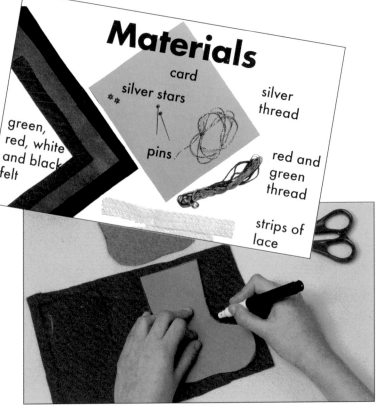

Materials

card

silver stars

pins

silver thread

green, red, white and black felt

red and green thread

strips of lace

1 Trace off the stocking on page 38 on to card and cut out to make a template.

2 Draw round the stocking template twice on the red felt and twice on the green felt. Cut out. Pin the red stockings together and the green stockings together.

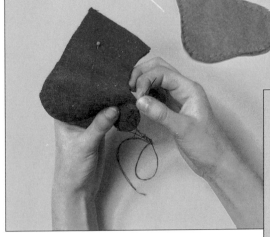

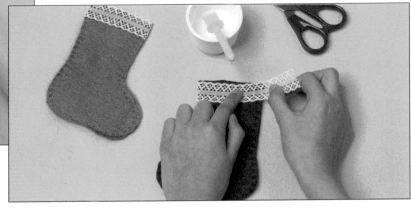

3 Sew an even line of running stitches around the stockings, leaving the tops open.

4 Cut 2 small pieces of lace to fit around the top of the stockings. Glue in place.

5 Cut 2 snowmen from white felt (template on page 38) and glue to the stockings. Mark faces and buttons with felt-tip pen.

6 Cut 2 hats from black felt (template page 38) and glue in place. Stick a silver star above the snowmen.

7 Sew a loop of silver thread through the top of each stocking. They can be hung from a tree and filled with small presents.

Make several stockings, one for each member of your family, and decorate each with a different Christmas design.

19

Materials

1 egg, beaten

boiled sweets broken into small pieces

liquorice laces

icing

2 teaspoons ground ginger

1 teaspoon ground cinnamon

cutters

gold and silver balls

100 g butter

4 tablespoons golden syrup

½ teaspoon bicardonate of soda

350 g plain flour

175 g soft brown sugar

Spicy Biscuits

This dough makes 35 biscuits. You'll find it easier to roll out in 2 halves.

1 Sieve the flour, spices and bicardonate of soda into a large bowl.

2 Cut the butter into small chunks and rub in between your fingers until the mixture looks like fine breadcrumbs. Stir in the sugar.

! **3** Warm the syrup in a saucepan until it is runny. Put the syrup and the beaten egg

into the bowl and mix together. Gather the dough into a ball and knead well until it is smooth.

4 Roll out half the dough on a lightly-floured surface until it is about 5 mm thick. Cut shapes from the rolled dough. Use a small round bottle lid to cut out the centre of some of the biscuits.

! **5** Make a hole at the top of each biscuit. Place on a baking tray covered with greaseproof paper and bake in a preheated oven at 190°C/375°F/Gas Mark 5.

! **6** After 4 minutes take the biscuits out of the oven. Make the hanging hole bigger. Put broken pieces of boiled sweet in the centre holes.

! **7** Return to the oven and bake for about 6 minutes more. When the biscuits are completely cold, peel off the greaseproof paper. Decorate with the icing and gold and silver balls.

Thread a liquorice lace through each hole to hang the biscuits from the tree. Make the biscuits a few days before Christmas and keep them in an air-tight container. Hang them on the tree on Christmas Eve.

Materials

gold thread

2 long pipe cleaners

metallic card

small yoghurt pots

2 bells

double-sided foil paper

silver foil

Three Tree Decorations

This year cover your Christmas tree with homemade decorations that sparkle and shine.

Silver bells

1 Trim around the edges of the yoghurt pots so that they are curved. Cover with foil.

2 Make a hole in the pots. Thread a bell on to each pipe cleaner. Twist the ends of the pipe cleaner together and push through the holes.

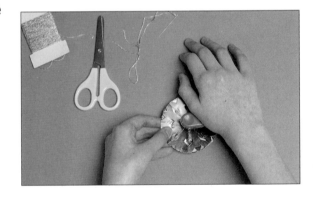

Foil snow flakes

3 Cut 8 circles from double-sided foil. Fold 1 circle in half and half again and half again. Snip shapes from the edges of the folded paper circle. Repeat with the other 7 circles.

4 Open out the cut circles. Put them together and staple in the centre. Open out into a ball. Sew a thread to the top for hanging.

22

Present boxes

The silver bells can be hung up individually or twist the pipe cleaners together to hang them as a pair.

! **5** Trace off the template on page 39 on to the shiny side of the card and cut out. Score lightly along the lines and fold over.

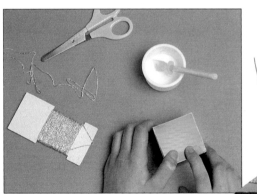

6 Put glue on the side tabs and press firmly in place inside the box. Glue the top tab to the outside of the box. Tie ribbon around the box in a decorative bow for hanging.

The dressed tree. To make the felt stockings, see page 18, and for the decorated biscuits see page 20.

Lantern Chains

Materials

shiny wrapping paper

red tinsel

Light up your living room this Christmas with these sparkly lantern chains.

1 Cut a piece of paper 11 x 15cm and fold in half lengthways.

2 Use pinking shears to make snips along the folded edge about 1cm apart, leaving 1cm uncut along the unfolded edge. Open out the paper.

Join the lanterns to the chain by making one of the strips into a handle. Thread it through the chain, then glue either end of the strip and stick to the top of the lantern. Make sure you space the lanterns evenly along the chain.

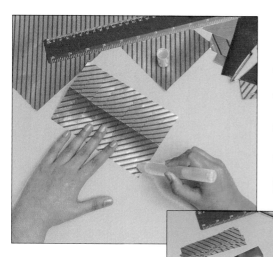

3 Put glue along a short edge. Curl the paper around and overlap the edges to stick together.

4 Cut a short piece of tinsel and push into the lantern to make a flame.

5 Cut several strips of paper 2 x 11cm from each of the sheets of shiny paper.

6 Make a loop with a strip and glue the ends together. Thread a different coloured strip through the loop and glue the ends together. Make the chain as long as you like.

All Chained Up

Materials

4 rolls of coloured crêpe paper

red and white sticky spots

40 x 10 cm strip of brown paper

You can make these chains as long as you need to fill your room.

Folded chains

1 Cut 3-cm wide strips from crêpe paper cutting through the whole roll. Glue 2 different-coloured strips together as shown in step 2. Leave to dry.

Concertina chain

2 Fold the strips over one another, back and forth, until the whole length is folded. To make the chain longer glue another 2 strips to the ends and continue folding. Glue the ends together. Trim and leave to dry. Pull out and hang.

3 Fold the strip of light brown paper into a concertina, making folds every 5 cm.

4 Trace the reindeer template on page 39 on to the folded paper and cut out.

26

To make a star chain, cut out card stars (template page 38). Decorate with silver foil and sequins. Use curled gift ribbon to tie them on to ribbon.

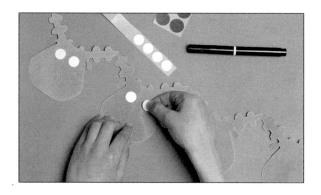

5 Unfold the paper. Stick the white dots on to each reindeer face to make the eyes.

6 Stick on the red dots to make noses. Finish off the mouth and eye details with a black felt-tip pen.

Reindeer Mask

1 Cut the plate in half. Tape a tracing of the mask template on page 39 to the rounded side of the plate. Draw around the eye holes and the bottom outline of the mask. Cut out.

2 Paint the rounded side of the plate brown. Leave to dry.

3 Cut 2 ears from the card. Paint brown and leave to dry, then paint the centre of the ears pink.

4 Cut 2 antlers exactly the same size from the card and paint both sides red. Leave to dry.

5 On the unpainted side of the mask, glue the antlers to the top and the ears to each side.

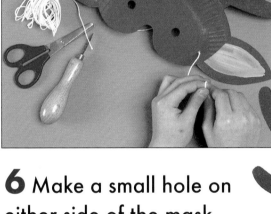

6 Make a small hole on either side of the mask. Tie a double knot at one end of a piece of elastic. From the front of the mask, thread the elastic through one hole to the other and secure with a double knot.

Christmas Tree Mask

Stick 2 card Christmas trees to the back of the mask. Decorate the trees with gold thread and small bead balls. Glue a paper frill or tinsel around the mask.

Spread a little Christmas cheer with this reindeer mask.

Robin Piñata

A *Christmas* party game that's fun for everyone.

Materials

corrugated cardboard

1 metre ribbon

large button

wrapped sweets

balloon

lolly stick

newspaper strips

orange and brown card

black felt

red and white tissue-paper

flour and water paste (see page 40)

! **1** Blow up the balloon and tie the end in a knot. Cover the balloon with paste and stick the newspaper strips all over. Add another 5 layers and leave to dry in a warm place for 24 hours.

! **2** Pierce the balloon at the top to let out the air. Remove the balloon. Mark and cut a large flap into the side of the papier mâché. Thread the ribbon through the hole at the top and pull out through the slit.

3 Make a hole in the centre of a corrugated cardboard circle and thread the ribbon through. Tie the lolly stick to the ribbon. Thread a large button on to the ribbon. Push the card circle back through the slit. Pull the ribbon up tight and tie in a knot at the top.

4 Fill with sweets.

5 Paint brown. When dry mark on the robin's red and white breast. Cut out red and white tissue-paper feathers and glue on to the robin.

6 Cut 2 wings from the brown card (template page 38) and glue on to either side. Cut 2 beaks and 2 feet from orange card (templates page 38) and glue in place. Add black felt circle eyes.

The finished robin makes a lovely decoration. When it's party time, hang the robin on a door frame. Your friends are blindfolded in turn and spun around. They try to hit the robin with a wooden spoon until it bursts scattering sweets across the floor.

Sparkly Garland

Don't just decorate the tree this Christmas. Why not decorate yourself too?

1 Cut 5 10-cm lengths from the silver tinsel and 5 10-cm lengths from the red tinsel. Cut 10 2-cm lengths of double-sided tape.

2 Fold each piece of tinsel in half and press a piece of double-sided tape on to it.

3 Attach a piece of silver tinsel 25 cm in from the end of the gold thread by removing the backing from the double-sided tape and folding the tinsel around the thread. Position all the silver tinsel pieces along the thread about 10 cm apart from each other.

4 Cut 8 30-cm lengths from the gold ribbon. Tie 2 pieces on to the gold thread between each piece of silver tinsel.

5 Push the gold ribbon close to the tinsel. Curl the ribbon with closed scissor blades.

Stick coloured tinsel on to hair slides, combs and hairbands to make some stunning sparkly bits for your hair.

6 Finally add the red tinsel pieces. Remove the backing of the double-sided tape and fold on to the gold thread between the gold ribbons.

7 Knot the ends of the thread together.

Materials

potato

carrot

tissue-paper

thick paper

Under Wraps

Two simple ideas for printing and stencilling your own wrapping paper.

Holly print paper

! **1** Ask an adult to cut a holly leaf shape from half a potato.

2 Dip the cut potato into green paint and print holly leaves on to tissue-paper.

Add sparkly detail to the wrapping paper with glitter and glitter glue.

3 Cut the end from a carrot. Dip into red paint and print berries next to the leaves.

Snow scene

4 Draw a circle on to thick paper and cut out.

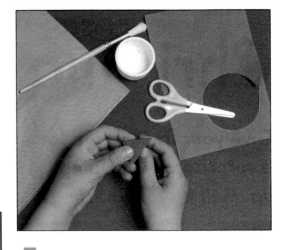

5 Fold the paper circle in half and half again and half again.

You can print matching gift tags on to folded card and attach to your presents with curled gift ribbon.

6 Cut out a pattern along the folded edges. Open out.

7 Use the cut circle as a stencil. Stencil white snowflakes on to coloured tissue-paper dabbing the paint over the cut areas.

Christmas Present

Give your friends and family a surprise by wrapping yourself up for Christmas.

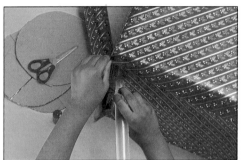

Materials

printed wrapping paper

large cardboard box

metallic paper

gift ribbon

Christmas card

! **1** Cut the flaps from the box. Cut holes for your arms and head. Cover with wrapping paper.

2 At the head and arm openings cut triangular tabs from the paper. Glue the tabs to the inside of the box.

3 For a decorative ribbon glue wide strips of metallic paper around the box.

4 Cut a large square of metallic paper. Fold over the edge of the paper by 2 cm and press down. Turn over and fold over by 2 cm again. Repeat until all the paper has been folded.

6 Punch a hole in the top left-hand corner of the Christmas card. Thread the ribbon through the hole.

5 Fold in half and staple the top 2 edges together to make a fan. Put a length of double-sided tape along the bottom of the fan, remove the backing and press down firmly on to the box to the side of the head hole.

Tie the Christmas card gift tag around your wrist.

Wear the Christmas present over an outfit of leotard and tights or sweatshirt and jogging bottoms.

To make a decoration for your hair, stick a rosette to a hair slide. Curl lengths of thin metallic ribbon along closed scissor blades and tie to the slide.

37

Templates

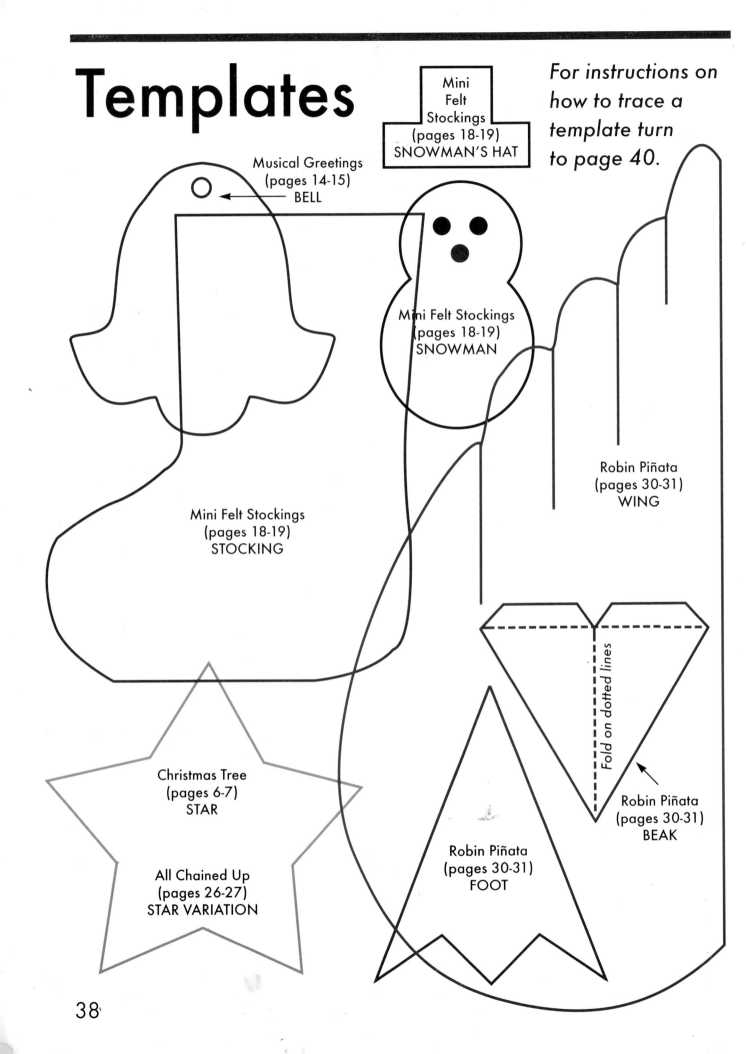

Mini Felt Stockings
(pages 18-19)
SNOWMAN'S HAT

For instructions on how to trace a template turn to page 40.

Musical Greetings
(pages 14-15)
BELL

Mini Felt Stockings
(pages 18-19)
SNOWMAN

Robin Piñata
(pages 30-31)
WING

Mini Felt Stockings
(pages 18-19)
STOCKING

Fold on dotted lines

Christmas Tree
(pages 6-7)
STAR

Robin Piñata
(pages 30-31)
BEAK

Robin Piñata
(pages 30-31)
FOOT

All Chained Up
(pages 26-27)
STAR VARIATION

38

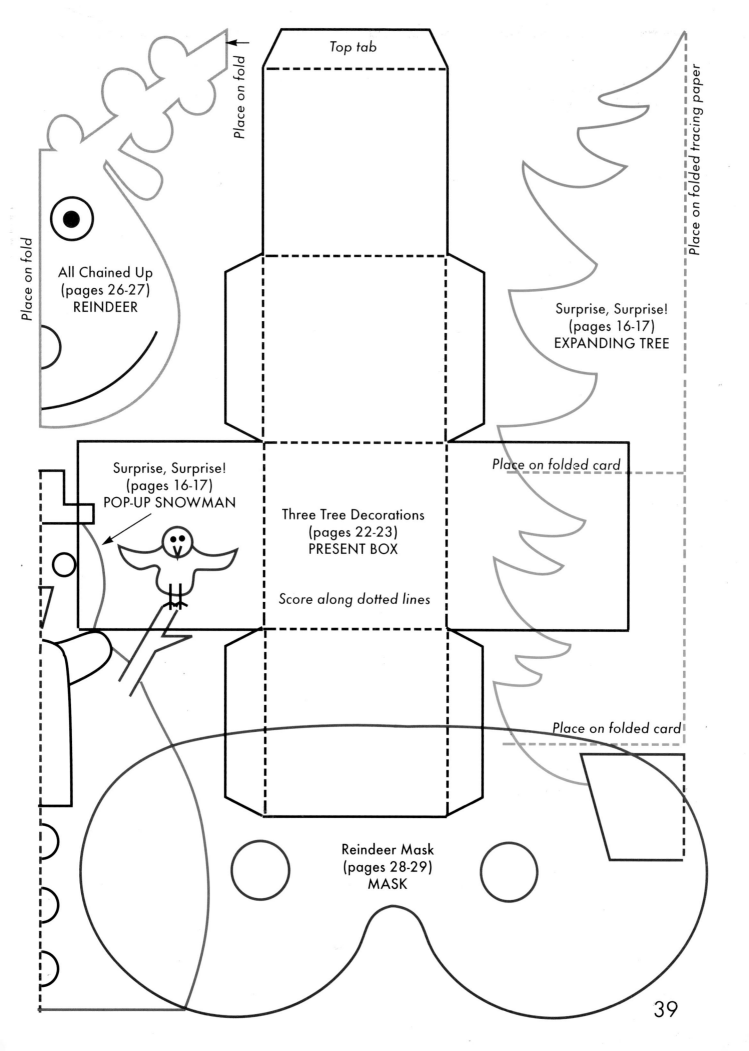

Top tab

Place on fold

Place on folded tracing paper

Place on fold

All Chained Up
(pages 26-27)
REINDEER

Surprise, Surprise!
(pages 16-17)
EXPANDING TREE

Place on folded card

Surprise, Surprise!
(pages 16-17)
POP-UP SNOWMAN

Three Tree Decorations
(pages 22-23)
PRESENT BOX

Score along dotted lines

Place on folded card

Reindeer Mask
(pages 28-29)
MASK

39

Advice to Parents

This book is filled with lots of simple ideas to occupy your children in the build up to Christmas, and to help them to be involved in the preparations. The information provided on this page is designed to help you to help them to get the most from the activities.

Tools and Materials

Paint From a small selection of paints – red, yellow, blue, black and white – all other colours can be obtained by mixing. Encourage your child to explore colour mixing for herself. Poster paints are ideal for painting all the projects in this book. Always ensure that paint has dried before going on to the next step in the project.

Felt-tip pens A set of felt-tip pens is a good idea for adding fine decorative details.

Glitter glue This is a quick and easy way to add decoration to Christmas projects. Glitter glue is available from large newsagents or stationers in pen or tube form in a wide range of colours from red and green to gold and silver.

Glue Solvent-free PVA adhesive is recommended as it is versatile, clean, strong and safe.

Scissors For the sake of safety children should use small scissors with round-ended metal blades and plastic handles. Although these are fine for cutting paper and thin card, they will not cut thick card and this is best done by you. This will often require a craft knife. Use a metal ruler to provide a straight cutting edge. If you do not have a cutting mat, use an old chopping board or very thick card to protect the work surface beneath. Regularly change the craft knife blade for a clean, sharp edge.

Bradawl An ideal tool for making a hole in card. Lay the card over a flattened ball of play dough or modelling clay and pierce with the bradawl.

Paper and card Try to keep both white and coloured paper in the house. Do recycle paper whenever possible. Make use of off-cuts of wallpaper for example. Coloured card can be expensive: old cereal packets, folded flat, are perfect when thin to medium card is needed. Simply paint the unprinted side of the card. For the Present boxes on page 23 you could make use of last year's Christmas cards, or cover off-cuts of scrap card with a Christmas wrapping paper.

Odds and ends box Encourage your children to collect bits and pieces throughout the year that might come in useful for making Christmas decorations – including the coloured foil from their Easter eggs! Give them a box to keep a collection in. Useful odds and ends include: cardboard tubes, yoghurt pots, bottle tops, jar lids, cereal packets, matchboxes, thick card, paper plates, sweet wrappers, tissue-paper, wrapping paper, colour magazines, felt, string, wool oddments, ribbon ends, lolly sticks, material off-cuts, tinsel, pipe cleaners, sequins, self-adhesive shapes, buttons and beads.

Salt Dough

Salt dough can be baked hard, painted and varnished so that your child can keep the things he makes. It is perfect for making tree decorations. We have used coloured salt dough in this book to make a holly wreath for the front door (see page 12). To make salt dough you will need to mix together 100 g plain white flour, 50 g salt and 1 teaspoon of cooking oil in a bowl. Add 80 ml of water that has had a tablespoon of red food colouring added to it to the ingredients a little at a time and mix to a smooth paste that leaves the sides of the bowl clean. If the dough becomes slightly tacky add a little

flour and work it into the mixture. Salt dough is best made the day before it is required. Store in a plastic bag in the fridge. Before using knead well on a lightly-floured board.

Before baking modelled articles, brush lightly with a little water to give a good finish. Place items on a lightly-greased baking tray or on silicon-finished baking parchment. Salt dough should be cooked slowly in the oven on a low heat (120°C/350°F/Gas mark ½). Small articles will take about 1-2 hours, larger models will need 3-4 hours. Better still, cook overnight on the lowest setting. If possible turn the salt dough items over halfway through baking to ensure that they are cooked through.

Papier Mâché

Papier mâché is made from old newspapers and a flour and water paste. To make this smooth, slightly runny paste you will need approximately 2 heaped tablespoons of plain white flour to 100 ml water. Gradually add the water to the flour and mix well. Do make sure that the papier mâché has dried out completely before decorating. This will take about 24 hours in a dry, warm place such as an airing cupboard. For the Robin Pinata on page 30 we have suggested that you cover the balloon with 6 layers of newspaper strips. Remember the more layers you add the stronger the papier mâché will be. If the game is to be played by very young children use only 3 or 4 layers so that the bird will be easier to burst; if the robin is primarily to be used as a decoration then put on more layers, as many as 8 or 9.

Making a Tracing

To make a tracing from the templates on pages 38-39 lay a piece of tracing paper over the required template. Draw around the outline with a pencil. Turn over the tracing paper and scribble over the pencil outline. Turn the tracing paper over once again and lay it down on to the paper or card that you want to transfer the tracing to. It is often a good idea to keep the tracing in place with masking tape. Carefully draw around the pencil outline. Remove the tracing paper. The outline of the traced shape on the card may be quite faint. Go over it with black felt-tip pen if necessary. It is a good idea to make a reusable template. Transfer the tracing on to thick card. Cut out and label the card template and keep it in a safe place. Use the card template to draw around as often as it is needed. To make a tracing of the Pop-up Snowman and Expanding Tree templates fold a piece of tracing paper in half. Lay the folded edge on the dotted line and trace around the outline. Turn the tracing paper over, and go over the outline firmly with a pencil to transfer it on to the other half of the tracing paper. Open up the tracing paper. The completed outline is now ready to be transferred on to card or paper in the usual way.

Safety in the Kitchen

If your child is going to make the biscuits and sweets featured in this book do encourage good kitchen practice. Always use oven gloves to remove cooked items from the oven, and make sure that they are left to cool down completely before decorating begins. Do note that the cooking time given for the Spicy biscuits (page 20) may vary slightly from oven to oven. Do keep an eye on them as they cook. If undercooked, the biscuits will be soft; if overcooked they may be too hard.